ON MORE F... & FINGER...

CLIMBING & WALKING CARTOONS BY JIM WATSON

ISBN 0902 363 96 4
First published 1987
Reprinted 1990, 1993

Published by Cicerone Press
Police Square, Milnthorpe, Cumbria

INTRODUCTION...

This is my second book of cartoons and its publication is entirely due to the reactions to the first.

There was the kind soul from Wastwater who invited me to 'drop in any time', the clean-up countrysider who dubbed the book 'more rubbish', and the local tourist board who offered me a free walking tour. In Beirut.

I'm grateful to you all! Audience participation is meat and drink to any humorist.

If you've bought this book or reading it in a bookshop while sheltering from the rain, thank YOU for reacting. Best of all, I hope you've smiled!

My drawing hand is tired and blistered, so I'm off to see how my feet react to some walking.

Now, how far is it to Wastwater.....?

Jim Watson RUGBY.1987.

THAT SNEEZE HAS
PROBABLY COST US
THE CLIMB

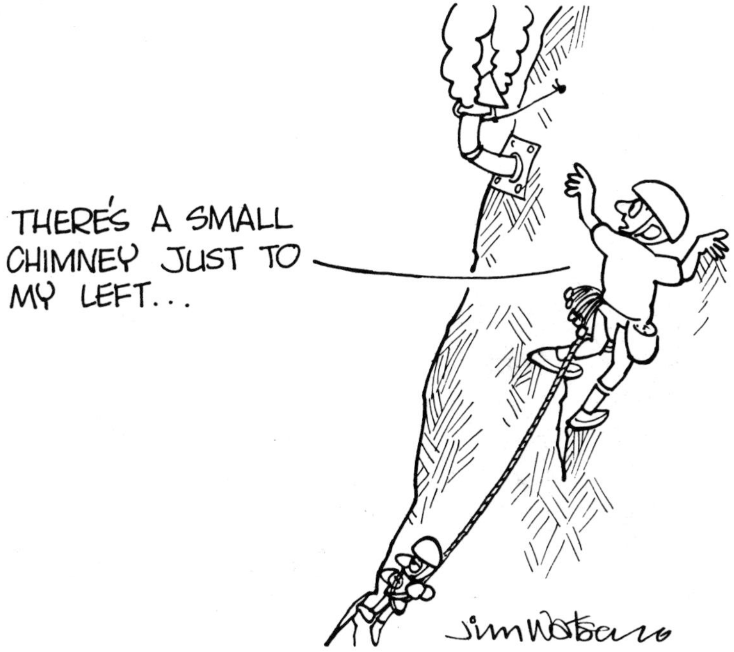
THERE'S A SMALL CHIMNEY JUST TO MY LEFT...

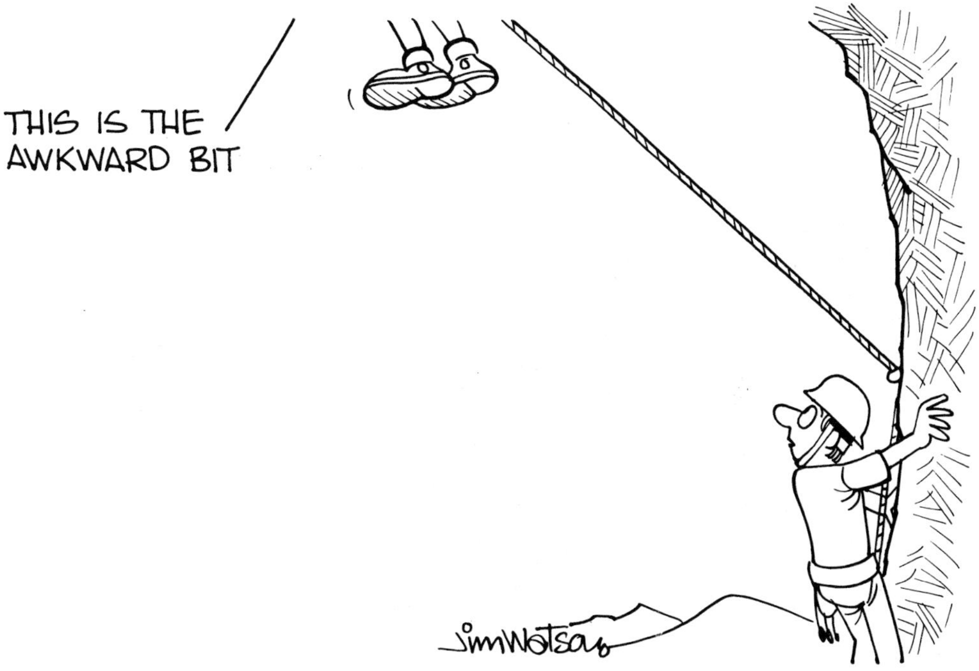
THIS IS THE
AWKWARD BIT
JimWatson

THIS IS GOING TO PLAY HAVOC WITH MY MILEAGE CALCULATIONS
PENNINE WAY

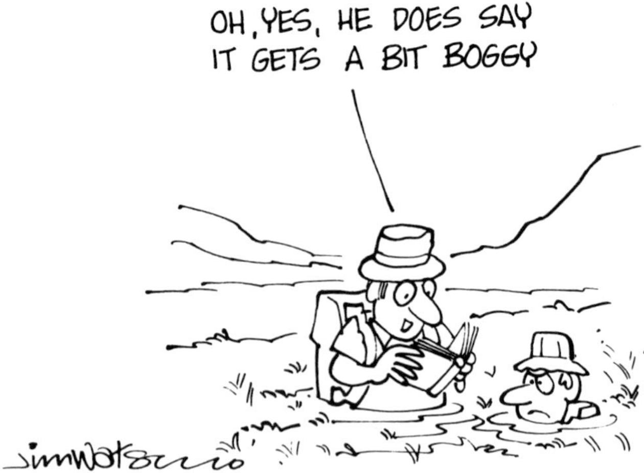
OH, YES, HE DOES SAY IT GETS A BIT BOGGY

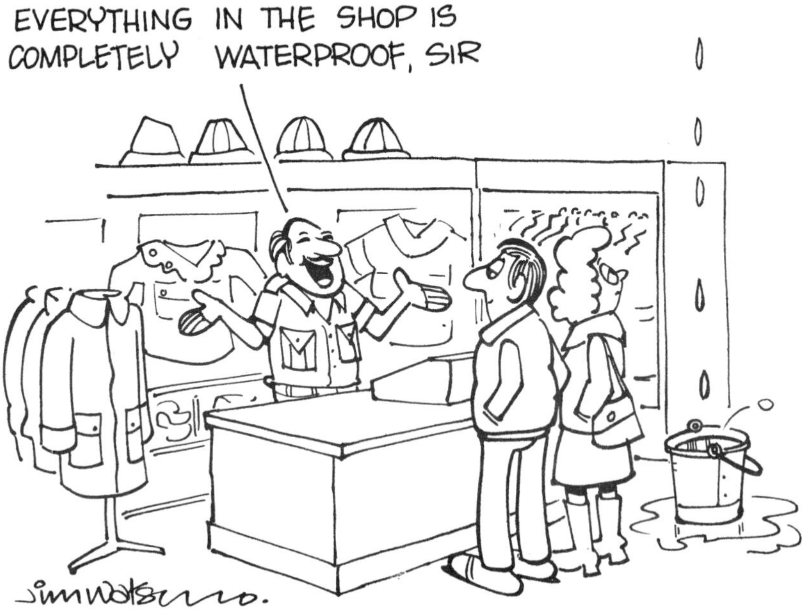
EVERYTHING IN THE SHOP IS COMPLETELY WATERPROOF, SIR

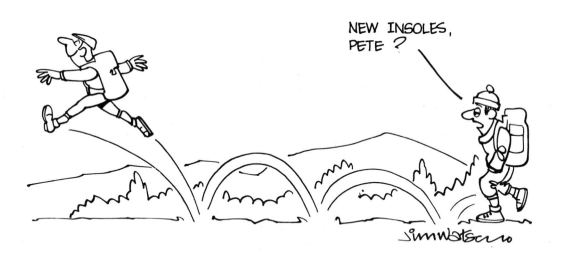

For **ANYTHING** drawn...

JIM WATSON
25 FROBISHER RD. RUGBY. CV22 7HU.